The Borrowers

A novelization by
SHERWOOD SMITH
Based on the screenplay by
GAVIN SCOTT and JOHN KAMPS
Based on the novels by
MARY NORTON

Level 2

Retold by Karen Holmes
Series Editors: Andy Hopkins and Jocelyn Potter

Pearson Education Limited
Edinburgh Gate, Harlow,
Essex CM20 2JE, England
and Associated Companies throughout the world.

ISBN 0 582 36399 3

Novelization first published in the USA by Harcourt, Brace & Company 1997
Published in Great Britain in Puffin Books 1997
This edition first published 1999
Third impression 2004

Published by arrangement with Harcout Brace & Company

Typeset by Digital Type, London
Set in 11/14pt Bembo
Printed in China
SWTC/03

Published by Pearson Education Limited in association with
Penguin Books Ltd, both companies being subsidiaries of Pearson Plc

For a complete list of titles available in the Penguin Readers series, please write to your local
Pearson Education office or to: Penguin Readers Marketing Department,
Pearson Education, Edinburgh Gate, Harlow, Essex CM20 2JE.

Contents

Introduction

'A Borrower meets a human being and the last thing he sees is a shoe. Then squash!' Pod said.

The Lender family are human beings and the Clock family are 'Borrowers'. They live happily together in an interesting old house. But a lawyer, Ocious P. Potter, wants to pull down the house. Can young Pete Lender and his little friends stop him?

The Borrowers are very small and very clever. They can climb, they make machines and they want to fight Ocious P. Potter before he squashes them!

8.6 million people watched *The Borrowers* on BBC television. Now it is a film. John Goodman is the bad lawyer, Ocious P. Potter, Jim Broadbent is Pod Clock and Flora Newbigin is Arrietty.

Mary Norton was an English writer. She wrote the first book about *The Borrowers* in 1952. She wrote five more stories about these very small people. Her book *Bedknobs and Broomsticks* was a favourite film for children.

Chapter 1   The Lenders

Pete Lender and his mother and father, Joe and Victoria Lender, lived in a big old house in a little town. Pete and his mum and dad liked the house. Before she died, Victoria's Aunt Mary lived there.

'Where are my brown shoes?' Joe asked one morning. 'I can't find them.'

'Wear your black shoes,' Victoria said.

'Where does everything go in this house?' Pete asked his mother. 'I can never find anything. The pen by the telephone, the Christmas tree lights, the safety pins and the dental floss and the matches. I think something takes our things, but what?'

Victoria and Joe had their best coats on. 'Where are you going?' Pete asked.

'We're going to meet an important man, Ocious P. Potter,' Joe said.

'He's a lawyer,' Victoria said. 'We're going to talk to him about the house.'

'Is something wrong?' Pete asked.

'No,' Joe said. 'I don't think it's anything important.'

Victoria looked at her watch. 'Let's go, Pete. You're going to be late for school.'

'I can't find my keys,' Joe said.

'Oh!' Victoria cried. 'Pete's right. Some – some – thing took them!'

'Yes!' Pete cried.

Victoria laughed. 'Here are the keys,' she said. They were in her hand all the time.

'Huh!' Pete said and the three of them went out of the door. Joe and Victoria climbed into their car and drove away. Pete got on his bike but he looked back at the house.

Chapter 2 The Borrowers

In the kitchen, on the floor, there was a very small man. He was only ten centimetres tall. He threw a safety pin up on to the table. On the safety pin was a white dental floss rope. The little man climbed quickly up the rope.

The little man's name was Pod Clock. He was as old as Joe Lender.

'I'm tired,' he said. 'I'm too old to climb.' He pulled up a small box after him. Inside the box was Arrietty Clock, Pod's daughter. She was as old as Pete Lender.

'Now stop there, Arrietty,' Pod said. 'What's the First Thing Borrowers Learn?'

Arrietty laughed. 'The First Thing Borrowers Learn? Is it "Be happy"?'

'Arrietty!'

Arrietty laughed again. 'The First Thing Borrowers Learn is

The little man's name was Pod Clock.

that nobody must see a Borrower. Can we go now?'

'Wait! Peagreen.'

Inside the box was Arrietty's brother, Peagreen. He was younger than Pete, only five years old.

'Come on, Peagreen. We have a big day,' Pod said.

'I don't like big days,' Peagreen said.

'You don't like anything,' Arrietty said.

'I like ice-cream −'

'What's the Second Thing Borrowers Learn?' Pod asked.

'The Second Thing Borrowers Learn,' Arrietty and Peagreen said together. 'Borrowers only borrow the things they must have.'

'And ice-cream,' Peagreen said.

'Some Borrowers take too much. My old friend Swag borrowed some fruit from a human being. He had to eat it every day for a month,' Pod smiled.

Arrietty looked at the kitchen. On the door of the refrigerator was a picture of Pete, Victoria and Joe. 'Are human beings *very* bad?'

'A Borrower meets a human being and the last thing he sees is a shoe. Then, squash!' Pod said.

Arrietty looked at the picture of Pete. 'The young human being is nice.'

'Young human beings are the worst. Arrietty −'

'Yes, Dad?'

'Stay here. Don't move.'

'Yes, Dad,' Arrietty said. She smiled.

Chapter 3   Ocious P. Potter

Joe and Victoria sat in the big office of Ocious P. Potter. Everybody in town called Mr Potter an Important Man. He wore an expensive jacket and he had a moustache. On his hand was an expensive watch.

'But we were here, in this office! "I want you to have the house,"
Aunt Mary said.'

'No letter?' Joe and Victoria said together.

'No. I looked for it,' Mr Potter said. 'There's no letter from your Aunt Mary.'

'But we were here, in this office! "I want you to have the house," Aunt Mary said. You were there!'

'Sometimes people say one thing and do something different. Your Aunt Mary said one thing and died. She didn't write a letter. I must sell your house.'

'But she loved the house and we love it too,' Joe said. 'Can't we do something!'

'You can't but I can,' Mr Potter said. He showed them a picture of a big building. 'Twenty-four expensive new flats in place of your old house. Isn't it nice? You must move out of that house on Saturday.'

'Saturday?' Victoria said. She started to cry.

'Twenty-four expensive new flats in place of your old house. Isn't it nice?'

5

Mr Potter watched Joe and Victoria walk slowly out of the building.

'What can we do?' Victoria asked sadly.

'There was no letter . . .' Joe was sad too.

'Pete's going to be very unhappy,' Victoria said.

Mr Potter smiled. He looked at the picture of the flats. Mr Potter loved them. 'Today Potter's flats,' the lawyer said. 'Tomorrow, Pottersville Town!'

Chapter 4   Danger for the Borrowers

Arrietty started to climb up the refrigerator in the Lenders' kitchen. It was very big.

'Where are you going?' Peagreen asked. 'We must stay here. Dad'll KILL you!'

'I'm going to find some ice-cream,' Arrietty said. 'You open the refrigerator door.'

She climbed inside the refrigerator. She walked over to the ice-cream, put her hand into it and put some into her mouth.

'Come on, Arrietty,' Peagreen said – but suddenly he fell and the refrigerator door closed!

'Dad!' he cried. 'HELP!'

Pod was across the kitchen. With his dental floss rope, he climbed up to Peagreen on top of the refrigerator door.

'Where's Arrietty?' Pod asked.

Peagreen looked at the refrigerator. 'In there. Is it . . . bad?'

'Yes, it's bad,' Pod said. There was a noise at the front door. The human beings were home! 'And now it's worse.'

He took Peagreen's hand and they jumped down from the refrigerator to the floor.

'*YAAAAAGH!*' Peagreen cried.

Arrietty started to climb up the refrigerator in the Lenders' kitchen.

'Go home, son,' Pod said quietly to Peagreen. 'Tell your mother everything is OK.'

Peagreen ran home. Pod ran back to the refrigerator and climbed back on to it.

Joe and Victoria came into the house. They were very sad. Victoria loved the house and she wanted to stay. *Clack!* She thought she heard a noise near the refrigerator. Joe heard the noise too. They looked at the refrigerator but they didn't see the little man.

There was a hole in the refrigerator door for ice.

Pod said, 'Now listen carefully. The human beings are back. Find the hole in the door and come out, quickly.'

Inside the refrigerator Arrietty climbed carefully over the food. She was very cold.

Victoria sat in a chair. 'What can we do?' she said.

'I don't know,' Joe said.

'Perhaps Mr Potter will say we can stay,' Victoria said.

'I don't think so.' Joe took two glasses from the cupboard.

'Now, jump!' Pod said. Arrietty jumped down into the ice-hole in the refrigerator door.

Joe went over to the refrigerator door for some ice. Pod put his hand up into the hole so that the ice did not come out.

'What's wrong with it?' Joe asked. He looked at the refrigerator door. It was OK. He turned away and suddenly the ice came out on to the floor.

Joe looked at the floor. He found some dental floss. 'Where did that come from?' he asked.

◆

Joe didn't see Pod and Arrietty. They ran through holes in the walls, down under the floor.

Under the floor, the Clock family had a nice warm home. In it they had a lot of borrowed things from the Lenders' house. They had the Christmas tree lights.

Arrietty and Peagreen's mother, Homily, was very unhappy.

'They're too young to be borrowers, Pod. I told you,' she said. 'She's a bad girl. Your dad was a bad boy, too. He and his friends – Minty Branch, Swag Moss, Dustbunny Bin.'

'You must stay at home,' Pod said to Arrietty. 'You were in danger. A Borrower is quiet. Nobody sees him, nobody hears him.'

Later, after dinner, the two young Borrowers went to bed. Arrietty sat in her room. She went to a picture on the wall. Behind the picture was a hole. She jumped into it.

Chapter 5   Arrietty and Pete

'We must move from this house,' Joe told Pete after dinner.

'But this is our home!' Pete said.

'It's Mr Potter's house now,' his dad said.

'I'm staying here!' Pete said. Pete loved the house. It was big and old and interesting.

Later, he sat in his bedroom. Suddenly he saw a small light inside the cupboard. Quietly he looked through a hole in the cupboard and he saw a small light – but then it was gone!

'Pete? Lost something?' It was his father.

Pete moved quickly away from the cupboard – and Arrietty jumped out and climbed on to the table.

'I don't want to move from this house,' Pete said.

'The new house won't be bad,' Joe said and went out of the room.

'The human beings are moving!' Arrietty said. 'This is important. I must tell my family.'

She turned and ran, but she hit a book. It fell on the floor with a *bang* – and Pete saw her!

Arrietty looked at the boy's face. He had dark hair and dark eyes. He was nice, she thought, but *very* big. Pete looked at the little girl. She was very small. Arrietty wanted to run, but Pete quickly put a glass over her.

'Go on, human being!' Arrietty cried.

'You can talk!' Pete said.

'Of course I can talk. Now go on and do it!'

'Do what?'

'Squash me,' Arrietty said. 'I know you're going to squash me.'

'Why do you want me to squash you?'

'I don't *want* you to squash me,' Arrietty said. 'But human beings squash us.'

'I knew somebody took our things but I didn't think it was little people,' Pete said.

'We didn't take them. We do not take things. We borrow. We are Borrowers and you are our human beings. You are here to give us things to borrow.'

'How many Borrowers are there?' Pete asked.

'My mother, Homily, my dad, Pod, and my brother, Peagreen.'

'We must move to another house,' Pete said unhappily.

'I know,' Arrietty said. 'I heard.'

'Before she died, Aunt Mary forgot to write a letter to say this is our house. So now it's Mr Potter's house and he wants to pull it down and build some flats here.'

Arrietty was afraid. 'This is bad, very bad.'

Chapter 6   The Letter

On Saturday, the Lenders started to move their things. Pete carried an ice-cream box. Inside it was the Clock family and all *their* things.

Pete climbed into the car and carefully put the ice-cream box between two books. Joe and Victoria got into the car and drove away from the house. Inside the ice-cream box, the Clocks all fell over.

'Human being, you're going too fast,' Pod said.

'Slow down, Dad,' Pete said.

But the Clocks all fell out of the ice-cream box on to the floor of the car. There was a hole in the floor of the car and Arrietty and Peagreen fell next to it.

'Dad, stop! Please! I'm ill! I want to get out,' Pete said suddenly.

'No,' Joe said. 'I can't stop now. We must get to the new house.' He drove faster. Then suddenly Arrietty and Peagreen fell through the hole, down on to the street!

Peagreen was dirty but he was OK. Arrietty and Peagreen stood up and started to walk back to the old house. They saw a big car drive up to the house and a big man with a moustache got out. He went into the house.

The Borrower children went through the walls and into their old home under the floor. They ran to the wall and looked through a small hole.

Mr Potter moved through the house from one room to the next. 'The old woman left the letter here in the old house,' Potter said. 'That letter says that she left the house and her money to Victoria.'

The two Borrower children watched him. In one room, he made a hole in the wall and pulled out a box. He opened the box and took out a letter. Arrietty and Peagreen read the words:

THE LAST LETTER OF MARY B. ALABASTER

'So there *is* a letter,' Arrietty said. 'The house is Victoria's, not this man's! We must get that letter and give it to Pete!'

'We can't, Arrietty. How can we take it from the big human being?' Peagreen asked.

'I don't know,' Arrietty said, 'but we must try.'

Mr Potter tried to burn the letter with a cigarette lighter.

In one room he made a hole in the wall and pulled out a box.

Click! Click! Click! But the lighter did not work. He put the letter on the floor and looked round for some matches.

'Come on,' Arrietty said quietly to Peagreen.

Mr Potter found some matches and turned back to the letter – and he saw it start to move across the floor!

'What the . . .?' he said. The letter went through a hole in the wall. He put his ear next to the wall and he heard somebody speak.

'Do you think he saw us?' Peagreen asked.

'No, I don't think so,' Arrietty said. 'We must take this letter to Pete.'

'No, Arrietty, we must wait for Mum and Dad,' Peagreen said.

'Peagreen,' his big sister said. 'We must get this letter to Pete before that bad human being pulls the house down!'

'Bad?' Mr Potter said angrily. 'Who's bad?' And he started to pull up the floor. Under the floor, Arrietty and Peagreen were very afraid. The roof of their home opened and they saw a big hand above them.

'Come on, Peagreen!' Arrietty cried. But Peagreen couldn't get away from the big hand.

'Arrietty . . .!' Peagreen cried.

Quickly, Arrietty took an old knife and pushed it hard into the big hand.

'*Yow!*' the lawyer cried and pulled his hand out fast. He pulled up some more of the floor. Under the floor he saw a very small house. 'Ugh,' he said. 'Something lives down there.'

He pulled out his phone. 'Jeff? Help!' he said.

Chapter 7   The Killing Machine

A car drove up to the house. On the car were the words: JEFF – I KILL EVERYTHING. A nice young man got out.

'There's something in my house. Something lives under the floor.'

'Hello,' he said to Mr Potter. 'What can I do for you?'

'There's something in my house. Something lives under the floor.'

'What is it?' Jeff asked.

'I don't know. That's your job. Start work – find them!' Mr Potter said.

Jeff went into the house with a big machine. From behind the wall, Arrietty and Peagreen watched him.

'Quick!' Arrietty said. She put a rope, some pins and the letter in her bag.

Jeff looked down into the hole in the floor. 'Borrowers!' he said. 'I thought they were only in stories.'

'Can you kill them?'

'Why kill them?' Jeff asked unhappily.

'They took something important from me, and nobody takes things from Ocious P. Potter!'

'Well, they're Borrowers, sir. They don't take things, they –' Jeff began.

'Do your job! Kill them! NOW!' Potter cried.

'OK,' Jeff said quickly. He put the machine into the Borrowers' home and turned it on.

'This machine burns everything. It's very bad,' Jeff said.

Mr Potter smiled. 'Burns?' he said. 'That's good.'

Under the floor, Arrietty and Peagreen climbed quickly through a hole in the wall. They arrived at a second hole. They watched and the machine stopped.

'Are they dead?' Mr Potter asked.

Jeff didn't hear him, so Mr Potter hit him on the arm – and Jeff turned with the machine. It burned the lawyer's face.

'*Youw!*' Mr Potter cried. '*Augh!*'

Arrietty and Peagreen watched and laughed.

Jeff didn't hear him, so Mr Potter hit him on the arm – and Jeff turned with the machine.

'Get off!' Mr Potter cried. 'It burns! *Aagh!* My face! Find those Borrowers!'

The Borrowers started to run away again. Jeff made holes in the wall with a knife. The knife caught Peagreen's jacket. Jeff pulled him out of the hole.

'Arrietty!' Peagreen cried.

Jeff moved the knife up fast and Peagreen flew up – and across the room.

Chapter 8   Up on the Roof

Peagreen flew up and up and *up*. He hit a light and held on to it. The floor was a hundred kilometres away now. Mr Potter looked up and saw him.

'Do something, do something!' the lawyer cried to Jeff.

Jeff turned on the light.

'*Ow!* It's hot!' Peagreen cried. Below him the big bad human being waited for him to fall. Peagreen looked up. He saw Arrietty in a hole above the light.

'Don't fall!' she said. She quickly threw him the rope from her bag and Peagreen caught it. Arrietty pulled him up and together they climbed out on to the roof of the house. For the first time, they looked up at the big blue sky and down at the roofs of the town.

Arrietty took her brother's hand and they climbed carefully over the roof. She saw the church far away across the town. 'Mum and Dad are near that church,' she said.

'Can't we stay here?' Peagreen said.

'No, we can't. Mr Potter will squash us. Now we must climb down on our rope,' Arrietty said.

Peagreen was afraid. 'I don't like you, Arrietty Clock,' he said.

Chapter 9   Where Are Peagreen and Arrietty?

Pete and his mum and dad arrived at the new house. It was small and very, very new. They didn't like it.

'Here we are – home,' Joe said.

Pete jumped out of the car. His mum and dad went inside the house. Pete opened the back of the car. He saw the ice-cream box and he looked for the Borrowers. They weren't there!

Then Pod and Homily came out from behind another box. 'Oh, you're OK!' Pete said. 'But where are Arrietty and Peagreen?'

'They fell out of the car!' Homily said and she began to cry.

Pod was angry. 'You did this, human being. We must find them. Take us back to the old house – now!'

Pete put them back in the box and got on his bicycle.

Victoria came out of the new house. 'Pete, what are you doing?'

'Nothing, Mum,' Pete cried and went off on his bicycle before his mum and dad could stop him.

♦

Back at the old house, Mr Potter was very, very angry. 'Look at me,' he said.

Jeff looked at him. Mr Potter's good jacket was dirty. His round face was red and his hair was black with smoke. 'You look OK,' Jeff said.

'Oh, shut up,' the angry lawyer said. 'Now find those Borrowers!'

Jeff went out to his car and brought a sleepy brown dog back into the house. 'Say hello to Mr Smelly.'

The dog made a bad smell, then he made another. 'That's bad,' Mr Potter said. 'What does that animal eat?'

'Cheese,' Jeff said. 'Find the Borrowers,' he told the dog. The dog took the two men into the front garden – and there they saw a policeman. They knew Policeman Steady.

'Good morning, gentlemen. It's a nice day.' Policeman Steady looked at the lawyer. 'What happened to your face?'

'What do you want?' Potter asked.

'I heard two men came into this house and there were noises,' Policeman Steady said.

'It's my house,' Mr Potter said. 'I can do anything here.'

'Is it, sir? I thought it was the Lenders' house. They're a nice family.'

'It's my house now,' Mr Potter cried, 'so go away!'

'Don't forget I'm a policeman,' Policeman Steady said quietly.

The lawyer was very angry. But Policeman Steady only said, 'You must put something on your face.'

Potter walked away with Jeff and Mr Smelly. The policeman left. Then Pete arrived on his bicycle and saw Jeff's car in front of the house. 'Oh no!' he said.

Chapter 10 The Milkman Calls

Pete, Pod and Homily stood inside the old house and looked down at their home under the floor.

'Oh, Pod,' Homily cried. 'The children . . .'

'It's OK,' Pod said happily. 'They're not here.'

'OK?' Homily said. 'Look at it, look at our beautiful home. Who did this?'

Pete saw something on the floor. It was a lighter with the name O. Potter on it. He showed it to the Borrowers.

'He did,' Pete said.

◆

On the roof, Arrietty and Peagreen took the rope – and jumped. *Whizz!* They went down to the next roof.

'*Wheeeee!*' Arrietty cried. She loved it!

'*Yooooowwww!*' Peagreen followed her. He was afraid. 'I'm going to be ill!' he cried.

They heard noises below and saw Mr Potter, Jeff and Mr Smelly in the garden. The dog looked up at them and began to jump.

Arrietty and Peagreen were afraid of the dog. Then Peagreen turned his head – and looked into the eye of a very big bird. He jumped. Arrietty tried to catch him but he fell off the roof.

'*Yaaaaaaagh!*' he cried and he fell head-first into a milk bottle.

Mr Potter saw him. 'Ah! Now I've got you!' the lawyer cried, but before he could pick up the bottle, he saw Policeman Steady.

'I'm happy to see you, Mr Potter,' Policeman Steady said. 'I have something for the burns on your face.'

Above, Arrietty saw Mr Potter and Jeff turn to the policeman. Quickly she climbed down the dental floss rope.

'I'm happy to see you, Mr Potter,' Policeman Steady said. 'I have something for the burns on your face.'

At the same time, the milkman arrived and started to pick up the milk bottles – and the bottle with Peagreen in it.

Mr Potter looked at the friendly policeman. 'Go away.'

Policeman Steady smiled. 'I only want to help, sir.'

The lawyer turned and looked at the milkman. He must get that bottle first!

'That's nice,' he said with a big smile. 'Thank you. But I can't stop now!'

Policeman Steady did not move. 'I'm happy to help, sir,' he said. 'Good luck with your face.'

Arrietty jumped off her rope. Too late! She and Mr Potter and Jeff watched the milkman pick up Peagreen's bottle and drive away with it.

Mr Potter, Jeff and Mr Smelly followed the milkman. Pete came out of the house, the Borrowers' box in one hand, and watched them.

Inside their box, Homily said, 'What is it, Pete?'

'I don't know. Mr Potter, the second man and a big dog are following the milkman.'

'Do you think . . .?' Homily said to Pod.

'Yes!' Pod said. Then he called to Pete, 'Come on, human being! Follow those other human beings!'

Chapter 11   Spud Spiller

Pete couldn't see Arrietty in the garden and she couldn't see her mother and father in the box. They went away. Arrietty began to cry.

Somebody spoke to her. 'Why are you crying?'

Arrietty jumped. 'Who are you?'

A Borrower boy sat down next to her.

'You're a Borrower!' Arrietty cried. 'I thought we were the only Borrowers in the world.'

'My name is Spiller. Spud Spiller.'

'I'm Arrietty Clock,' she said. 'Can you help me find my brother?'

'He's gone to the milk factory,' Spiller said. 'You can walk there but it takes a long time. We can get there faster. Come with me.'

He helped her down into a hole under the garden. He showed her a matchbox and some safety pins. 'This is my car,' he said. 'It goes very, very fast.'

Spud and Arrietty arrived at the milk factory at the same time as the milkman with Peagreen's bottle.

Peagreen was afraid. The milkman carried the bottles into the factory but he didn't see Peagreen. He put the bottles on to a big machine and they started to move in a long line.

Spud and Arrietty ran into the milk factory.

'What's happening?' Arrietty asked.

'They bring the bottles in here, wash them, put more milk into them and send them out again. Borrowers can drink a lot of milk in this place!'

'Peagreen doesn't like milk,' Arrietty said.

'It's OK. We'll find him —'

Spiller stopped. He heard something – 'Help! Help!'

'That's Peagreen!' Arrietty cried.

They saw Peagreen's bottle and started to run.

The bottle moved slowly into the big bottle-washing machine. The machine made a lot of noise and it put a lot of water into the bottle. Peagreen started to cry. Then his bottle moved and he saw a second machine, a very hot machine . . .

Chapter 12   Inside the Milk Factory

Mr Potter, Jeff and Mr Smelly arrived at the milk factory. They did not see Pete arrive on his bike. He watched them run inside

The bottle moved and milk rained down on him.

the front door, then he picked up the Borrowers' box and followed them. He got as far as the door but Mr Potter closed it from the inside.

♦

Inside the milk factory, Arrietty and Spiller put some paper under the machine. They saw Peagreen.

'Arrietty!' he cried.

'You must jump!' Arrietty said.

'Oh *noooo*,' Peagreen cried. The paper was very small but it was better than the machine. Peagreen jumped out of the bottle and Arrietty and Spiller caught him in the paper. He sat up. 'I'm hungry,' he said. 'Who are you?'

'I'm Spiller,' said the new Borrower. 'But you can call me Spud. Who are you?'

Peagreen's trousers were wet. 'Hello, Spud. I'm *Peagreeeeeeeen*!' he cried. He fell through the paper and into a second milk bottle on the machine. 'Help! I don't like this place!' he said.

Spiller took his rope and threw it inside Peagreen's bottle. Peagreen picked up the rope but then he lost it. The bottle moved and milk rained down on him.

Peagreen swam up through the milk but then – *wham! snap!* – the machine closed the bottle.

From a window Pete, Pod and Homily watched. 'Pete, put us down near the door!' Pod said.

Pete put their box on the floor. He couldn't get through the closed door but the Borrowers could get under it.

Suddenly they heard something. Mr Potter started to break the bottles on the machine! Arrietty and Spiller saw his angry face and they started to run along the line of bottles.

Pod and Homily ran in and saw Peagreen in his bottle. Homily threw a rope round Peagreen's bottle. Pod climbed up the rope and kicked the bottle. It fell on the floor and broke. Pod

Homily threw a rope round Peagreen's bottle.

Mr Potter broke more and more bottles. 'I'll kill you!' he cried.

climbed in and found Peagreen. He did not move. Was he dead?

'Come on, son,' Pod said.

Peagreen opened his eyes. 'I don't like milk,' he said.

Behind them, Mr Potter broke more and more bottles. 'I'll kill you!' he cried.

Spiller threw his rope on to the machine and he and Arrietty pulled hard.

Zoink! zoink! zoink! Mr Potter heard a noise and stopped. Hundreds of kilos of cheese fell on Mr Potter's head. He fell. Arrietty and Spiller laughed at him. Now the Potter human being could not move.

The bottles on the machine moved past his head and the bottles hit him one by one. *Plink! Plonk! Clonk!* Spiller and Arrietty laughed harder and harder.

There was a second noise. Mr Smelly began to eat the cheese. *PH-H-H-H-HT!* He made a very bad smell.

Hundreds of kilos of cheese fell on Mr Potter's head.

◆

Arrietty and Spiller ran across to Pod, Homily and Peagreen. 'Who's this?' Pod asked.

'This is Spiller,' Arrietty said, smiling. 'He helped us.'

Somebody walked quietly up behind them. The Borrowers looked up and saw a cheesy, very ANGRY Mr Potter. 'That's nice – the whole family, together at last,' he said. 'I'll take that letter now.'

He took the letter from Arrietty's bag. Then he picked up the Borrowers in his hand.

Chapter 13   Help!

The lawyer put the five Borrowers in a big cheese box. They could not move. Then he turned on a machine. Above their heads they heard a noise. *Glorp! Blurp!*

'Hey, Cheese Face!' Spiller cried.

Mr Potter looked at him.

'What did you say?' Mr Potter said.

'I'm talking to you, fat man,' Spiller said. 'Because you're big, you think you can do anything.'

'I can,' Mr Potter laughed.

'Oh yeah? You can't get a girlfriend, you know, not with all that cheese on your face.'

The lawyer was very angry. He pulled Spiller out of the cheese box and pushed him into a hole in the machine. The machine made a lot of noise.

'*Nooo!*' Arrietty cried.

Mr Potter turned to the Borrowers. 'In one minute a lot of cheese will fall into that box,' he said. 'I want to watch you die, but I must go.' He walked out of the door.

Outside Pete ran into Mr Potter. 'Wait! Where are my friends?'

The lawyer pushed him away. 'I'm making your friends into cheese!' He jumped into his car, opened the car window and called to Jeff, 'Are you coming?'

Pete didn't wait to listen to the answer. He ran to find his friends.

Inside the car, Mr Potter looked for his lighter. He wanted to burn the letter but then he remembered that the lighter was at the old house.

♦

'How can I get into the milk factory?' Pete thought, then he saw a big hole in the wall and climbed through.

Where were the Borrowers? He saw the cheese machine. He had ten seconds before the cheese fell into the box. Ten . . . Nine . . . He climbed on to a machine. Three . . . two . . .

Voink! Voink! Voink! Red lights went on and off. In the box, the Borrowers could not move. Pete pushed the cheese machine and a lot of cheese fell on the floor.

Pete looked into the cheese box. Pod smiled at him. 'I'm very happy to see you, human being.'

Pete smiled and took the Borrowers out of the box.

'Pete, Mr Potter has the letter and he's going to the Town Hall,' Pod said. 'We must stop him. Run! We'll meet you at the Town Hall.'

Chapter 14   At the Town Hall

Outside the factory, a car stopped behind Pete. It was Jeff.

'I must get to the Town Hall,' Pete said.

'Jump in!' Jeff said. 'I'll take you. Where are the Borrowers?'

'They're going to meet us at the Town Hall,' Pete said.

'How are they getting there?' Jeff asked.

Under the milk factory, Homily, Pod and Peagreen sat behind Arrietty in Spiller's car. They went very, very fast along the Borrowers' 'roads' under the town.

◆

Mr Potter's car stopped outside the Town Hall. Policeman Steady walked slowly round the car. He was happy and he smiled.

'Hello, hello, hello,' he said. 'We meet again.'

'What do you want?' Mr Potter asked.

'You can't stop your car here, sir. You must stop down the road,' said Policeman Steady.

Potter moved the car back down the road. It ran over the policeman's bicycle. Then he drove away.

Policeman Steady watched him. 'I don't like that man,' he said.

Mr Potter ran up the steps of the Town Hall and spoke to a woman at the door.

'Quick!' he said. 'I want to pull down a house. Who do I talk to?' He did not say please. The woman did not like him.

'Go inside. Turn right, through the door, go up to the fourth floor, then walk up to the eighth floor, turn left and then turn right . . .'

Mr Potter's face turned redder and redder.

'. . . then turn left again. Go to the eleventh floor, turn right and look for the office there.' The woman smiled. 'You'll see it.'

'I want to get there quickly,' Mr Potter said.

'Then walk quickly,' the woman said.

♦

Jeff's car stopped outside the Town Hall. He and Pete ran into the building and spoke to the woman.

'Where do I go about pulling down a house, please?' Pete asked.

The woman smiled at him. 'Take the lift to the eleventh floor. You'll see the office.'

'Thank you,' Pete said.

'That's OK,' the woman said. Pete and Jeff ran to the lift. 'What a very nice boy,' she said.

♦

Mr Potter arrived at the eleventh floor and saw Jeff and Pete outside the door.

'Aha!' the lawyer said. He looked at Jeff. 'What are *you* doing?'

'I want to stop you from doing the wrong thing,' Jeff said.

Mr Potter laughed and pushed them away. 'You're going to stop me? How?'

Pete looked at Jeff and Jeff looked at Pete.

'Uh, I don't know,' Jeff said.

Mr Potter pushed them back into the lift and sent it DOWN . . .

Chapter 15   The Fight for the Letter

Mr Potter found the right office but nobody was in there. He turned to leave but the door closed. He could not get out.

'OK,' he said. 'Who's in here?' Nobody answered.

He moved back and fell. Behind him, Pod threw a safety pin at Mr Potter's back.

'*YYYOOOOWWWWW!*' Mr Potter jumped up.

He did not see Arrietty and Pod climb up next to him. They had a rope. They ran round and round Mr Potter with the rope and soon he could not move.

'I don't like you little people,' Mr Potter said.

Pod climbed down into Mr Potter's coat.

'Got it,' Pod said. He had the letter.

Arrietty helped him climb back on to the man's head. They did not see Mr Potter break the rope. Now he could move his arms. He took the letter and then he picked up the four Clocks in his hand and put them on the floor. He quickly put a waste paper basket over them and they could not move!

'Now, I'm going to kill you!' Mr Potter said.

But then he looked up. Eight Borrowers came at him down ropes. They wore big hats over their faces.

'What the . . .?' Mr Potter said.

The Borrowers ran quickly round him with a rope and, a minute later, he had rope from his nose to his feet.

'Get . . . these . . . ropes . . . OFF ME!' he cried.

The Borrowers on the floor picked up the waste paper basket and the Clocks came out. One of the Borrowers took off his hat.

'Spiller!' Arrietty cried happily. 'You're not dead!'

Three other Borrowers took off their hats.

'It's Minty, Swag – and Dustbunny Bin!' Pod said.

'We want to help,' Minty said.

Mr Potter made a lot of noise behind them.

He quickly put a waste paper basket over them and they could not move!

There were hundreds — no, thousands — of Borrowers round the lawyer.

'Don't move and be quiet,' Spiller said to him.

'I'm not afraid of twenty little people,' Mr Potter cried. 'I'll squash you!'

Spiller laughed. 'Twenty?'

Borrowers came out from every box all round them. Mr Potter and the Clocks watched more and more Borrowers arrive. There were hundreds — no, thousands — of Borrowers round the lawyer.

Minty said, 'Go on, Pod.'

The thousands of Borrowers were quiet. Pod walked up to Mr Potter.

Chapter 16   Policeman Steady Arrives

Pod climbed on to the lawyer's face.

'Listen, human being,' he said and he looked into Mr Potter's eyes. 'We're not bad little people. We are Borrowers. You thought we were dead but look at us. We're small but you can't squash all of us. Borrowers are good people. They're quiet. They're good friends. They're good climbers . . .' Pod touched Potter's red nose. 'We know you. We can find you again when we want you. Understand?'

Then the Borrowers heard a loud noise outside the room: *clonk, clonk, clonk*. Thousands of Borrower heads turned to look at the door. Somebody opened it.

Policeman Steady walked into the room. Pete was behind him. The lawyer was on the floor. There were no ropes round him now. 'Borrowers . . .' he said quietly.

Pete took the letter from Mr Potter's coat. Mr Potter didn't move. 'Here it is. He has the letter,' Pete said. 'He wanted to take our house.'

Policeman Steady looked at the letter. Then he looked at Mr Potter. 'What have you got to say, sir?'

Mr Potter said quietly, 'Borrowers. Thousands of little Borrowers . . . Very good climbers.'

Policeman Steady looked at Pete. Pete smiled. The policeman took Mr Potter's arm and took him out of the building.

Chapter 17   Home Again

An hour later Mr Potter sat at a desk in the police station. Policeman Steady sat near him.

'Little people, you say?' Policeman Steady asked.

Mr Potter was afraid. 'I told you. Millions of them!' Policeman Steady smiled. 'Do they have little houses with little tables and little chairs?'

'Yes,' Mr Potter said slowly. 'They do.'

Everybody in the room laughed at him.

♦

'Little people, you say?' Policeman Steady asked.

That night, Policeman Steady sat in the old house. There were a lot of boxes of the Lenders' things on the floor but there was a lot of food on the table and the house was warm.

With Joe, Victoria, Pete and Policeman Steady were Jeff and Mr Smelly. The dog sat happily on the floor.

After dinner, Joe Lender stood up. 'I want to say a big thanks. You helped us to stop Mr Potter. Thanks to Pete and our new friends, everything is OK now. Thank you.'

Pete took some vegetables off his plate, and went to the kitchen. He pushed the vegetables one by one through a small hole in the floor.

Below the floor Peagreen stood by the table. He caught the vegetables and put them on a plate.

Behind him the Clocks and their friends sat around the table. There were a lot of boxes of *their* things on the floor, but there was a lot of food on the table – thanks to Pete.

Pod and his friends, Minty, Swag and Dustbunny Bin told stories about the old days. Arrietty looked at Spiller. Spiller looked at Arrietty. They put down their knives, stood up and walked to the door.

Homily looked up. 'Where are you two going?'

'We're going to walk round the garden, Mum,' Arrietty said.

'OK, love,' Pod said. 'Have a good time.'

'We will,' Arrietty said. She turned and smiled.

They left the room. Spiller took her hand and they went to find his very, very fast car.

ACTIVITIES

Chapters 1–5

Before you read

1 Find these words in your dictionary. They are all in the story.

   dental floss   hole   human being   ice   ice-cream   lawyer
   matches   refrigerator   rope   safety pin   squash   wall

   Which one(s):

   a do we find in a refrigerator?

   b help you to climb up a wall?

   c are people?

   d make something smaller?

   e help us to clean our teeth?

   f help us to make a fire?

   g can you look through?

   h can you open and close?

2 This is a story about the Borrowers. These very small people live inside our houses. Not everybody can see them. Do you have any stories about little people in your country? What are they?

After you read

3 Who says these words? Who to? What is happening?

   a 'I'm too old to climb.'

   b 'There's no letter from your Aunt Mary.'

   c 'Today Potter's flats. Tomorrow, Pottersville Town!'

   d 'I'm going to find some ice-cream.'

   e 'Squash me. I know you're going to squash me.'

4 What problem do the Lenders have? Why is this also a problem for the Borrowers? Does Ocious P. Potter want to help them?

Chapters 6–11

Before you read

5 Find these words in your dictionary. Use them in the sentences.

   burn   cheese   lighter   machine   pick up   roof   smell

   a There's a very bad ...... Is something ..... in the kitchen.

b Can I borrow your ..... for my cigarette?

c Help! I'm on the ..... and I can't get down!

d Do you want ..... with your bread and butter?

e Turn off the ...... We're going home.

f Please ..... my pen. It's under your chair.

6 The Borrowers see something. It will help the Lenders with their problem. What is it?

After you read

7 Answer these questions.

    a What does Mr Potter want to do with Aunt Mary's letter?

    b Why does Mr Potter telephone Jeff?

    c Who is Mr Smelly and what does he eat?

    d How does Peagreen get away from Mr Potter?

    e Where is Peagreen at the end of Chapter 11?

8 Look at your house or classroom. What can the Borrowers use? Find three things. What will the Borrowers do with these things?

Chapters 12–17

Before you read

9 How will the story end?

10 Read this.

> *You find lifts in big buildings. They carry people. They stop at every floor of the building.*

What is a *lift* in your language? Look in your dictionary.

After you read

11 How do the Borrowers get the letter from Ocious P. Potter?

12 What will happen to these people now?

    a The Lenders

    b The Clock family

    c Spud and Arrietty

    d Ocious P. Potter

Writing

13 You are Mr Potter. At the police station, Policeman Steady tells you to write your story.

14 You are Pod Clock. It is two weeks later. Write a letter to your friend Minty. Thank him. Tell him about the Lenders, your family and Mr Potter.

15 Write about one of these:

    a Arrietty Clock

    b Pete Lender

    c Jeff and Mr Smelly

    d Ocious P. Potter

16 Write about the book for a friend. Tell the story. What did you like about it? What did you not like?